THE WAR OF THE WORLDS

by H. G. Wells

retold by Davis Worth Miller
and Katherine McLean Brevard

illustrated by José Alfonso Ocampo Ruiz

colour by Jorge Gonzalez/Protobunker Studio

LIBRARIAN REVIEWER
Katharine Kan
Graphic novel reviewer and Library Consultant

READING CONSULTANT
Elizabeth Stedem
Educator/Consultant

www.raintreepublishers.co.uk
Visit our website to find out
more information about
Raintree books.

To order:
☎ Phone +44 (0) 1865 888066
🖹 Fax +44 (0) 1865 314091
💾 Visit www.raintreepublishers.co.uk

Raintree is an imprint of Capstone Global Library Limited, a company incorporated in
England and Wales having its registered office at 7 Pilgrim Street, London, EC4V 6LB –
Registered company number: 6695582

"Raintree" is a registered trademark of Pearson Education Limited, under licence to
Capstone Global Library Limited

Art Director: Heather Kindseth
Graphic Designer: Kay Fraser
Edited in the UK by Laura Knowles
Printed and bound in China by Leo Paper Products Ltd

ISBN 978-1406212587 (hardback)
13 12 11 10 09
10 9 8 7 6 5 4 3 2 1

ISBN 978-1406213607 (paperback)
14 13 12 11 10
10 9 8 7 6 5 4 3 2 1

British Library Cataloguing in Publication Data
Miller, Davis.
The war of the worlds. -- (Graphic revolve)
741.5-dc22
A full catalogue record for this book is available from the British Library.

Table of Contents

Introducing . . .

The Martians

The Brother

The Artilleryman

The Curate

Ogilvy

Mary

George

In the last years of the 19th century, our world was observed by jealous eyes . . .

CHAPTER 1
FALLING STAR

. . . and plans were made against us.

Woking, England, 1894.

Six years later, April 1900 . . .

It's here!

The meteor is finally here!

Early the following morning, Ogilvy set out towards London with the idea of finding it.

Find it he did!

Why, this doesn't look like a meteorite!

10

That evening, I opened my daily paper, unaware of the situation nearby.

TRIBUNE

MEN FROM MARS LAND AT WOKING!

Oh, my!

Soon, the entire town was gathered at the edge of the great crater.

CHAPTER 2
FROM INSIDE THE CYLINDER

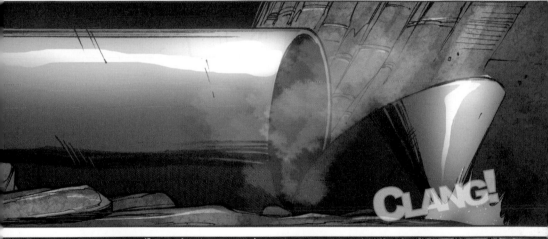

I stood frozen as a creature with a giant beaming eye rose out of the cylinder.

Then, a long, thin rod rose up, at the top of which a disk spun with a wobbling motion.

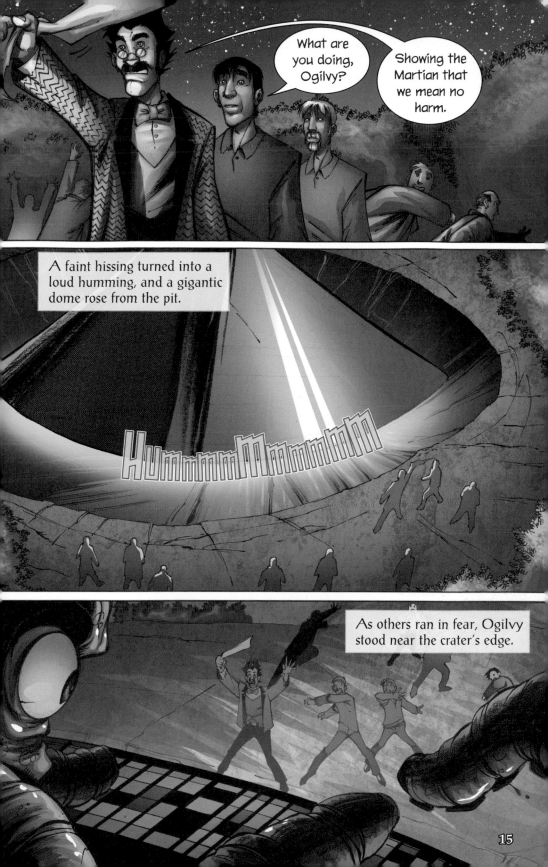

Then suddenly . . .

Ahhh!

HUMMMMMMMMMM

Help!

Flames leapt from one person to the next, as if each were instantly turned into a column of fire.

Let's get out of here!

Whoosh!

I stood frozen, too frightened to move.

Ogilvy!

WhoOsh!

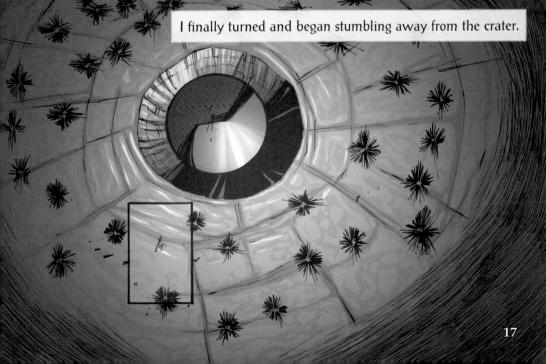

I finally turned and began stumbling away from the crater.

At midnight, another star fell from the sky.

Look!

It was a second cylinder.

KA-BOOM!

We have to get out of here!

The fighting with the Martians had begun!

Moments later, we tore down the road towards my cousin's house in Leatherhead, ten miles to the east.

Behind us, all of Woking was on fire from the Martian's heat ray.

CHAPTER 3
THE WAR BEGINS

The next day, we arrived at my cousin's house.

I read about the cylinder in the paper.

Thank goodness, you're all right!

It's worse than you can imagine!

The truth is I'd been excited all day, struck with a kind of war-fever. I wanted to see the end of the Martians.

21

23

The Martian fighting machine burned everything *alive!*

Good Heavens, man, sit and rest.

Thank you, sir, but I need to rejoin my company.

Far in the distance stood three fighting machines. Their hoods spun around as they examined the destruction they'd made.

My younger brother
was living in London.

CHAPTER 4
THE BATTLE FOR LONDON

The morning after I had seen the fighting
machines, he was suddenly awoken.

The Martians
are coming! Get
out now!

Six million people left London without food or supplies and with nowhere to go.

My brother made it to the coast, where he paid his way onto a steamboat to take him to Belgium.

Come aboard!

We'll get you all to safety.

Oh, no!

They're following us!

31

Then suddenly . . .

Look!

It was the fighting ship, *Thunder Child*, steaming to the rescue.

BLAM!

BLAM!

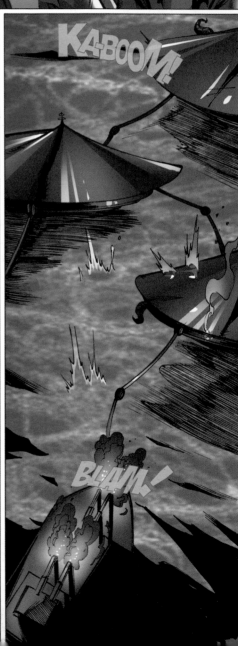

KA-BOOM!

BLAM!

The Martians retreated, rushing towards the shore. Suddenly, the middle Martian was struck by a shell and fell.

After a moment, a second machine crumpled like a cardboard toy.

That's two!

Yeah!!

All this time, the steamer had been paddling away from the fight. Soon, nothing could be seen of the third Martian.

Then suddenly, something flat and wide and dark swept along the shoreline.

It was the dreaded Black Smoke!

The curate and I hid in the ditch, too frightened to move or speak.

After hours of sneaking in and out of bushes, the curate and I reached an abandoned house.

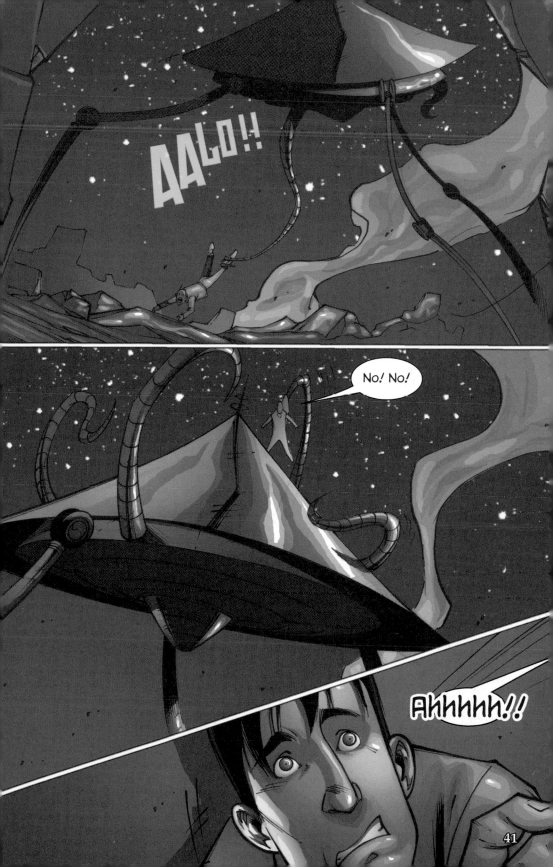

41

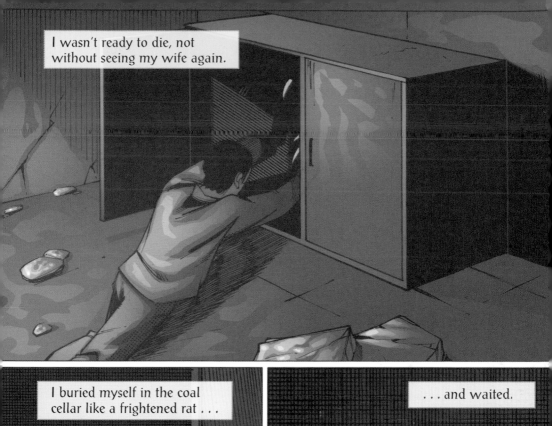

I wasn't ready to die, not without seeing my wife again.

I buried myself in the coal cellar like a frightened rat . . .

. . . and waited.

Soon, I heard the tentacle groping at the cellar door.

SLUUURM

SLUUURF

Then, it slithered inside, only inches from my face.

I followed the dog as he left the abandoned house.

I could hardly believe my eyes.

I had to see what lay beyond the crater's edge.

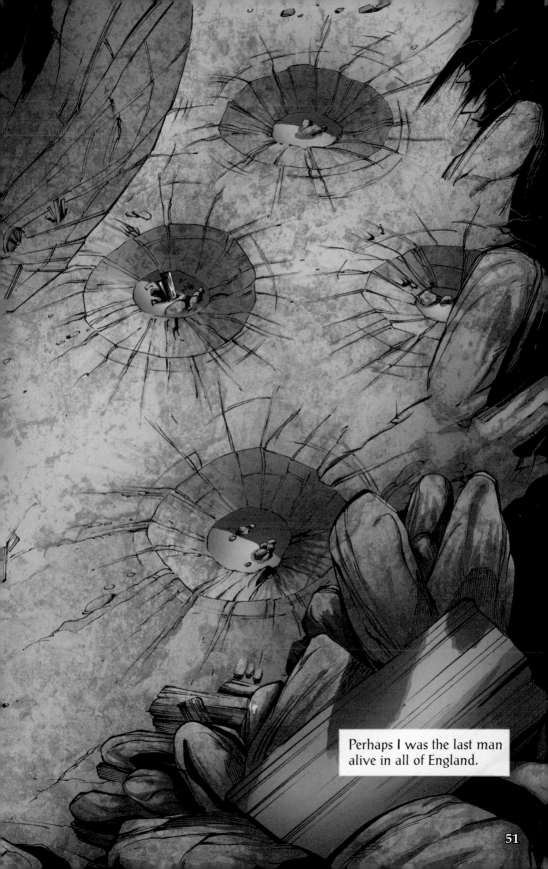

Perhaps I was the last man alive in all of England.

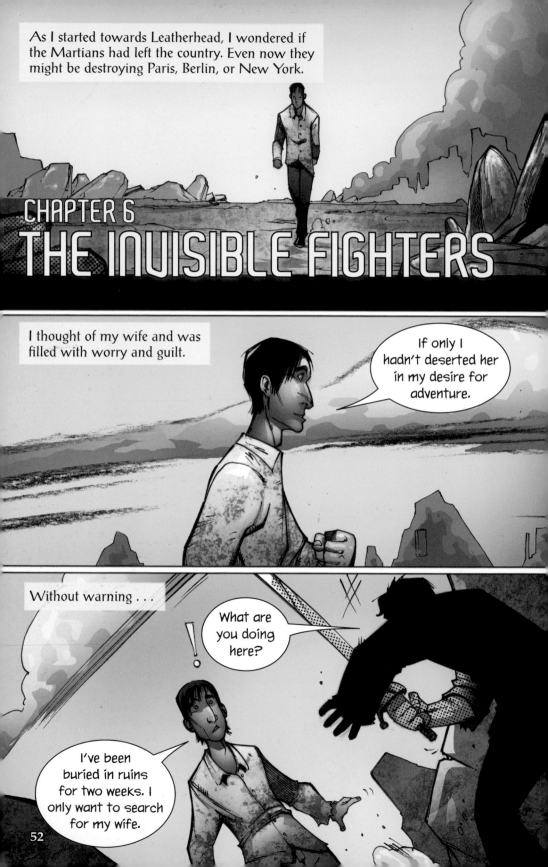

53

SMASH!

54

55

As I neared London, everywhere along the road was black dust, ruin, and a terrible stillness.

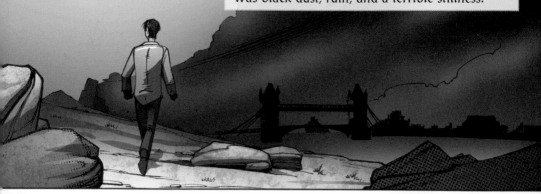

The further I went into the city the quieter it became.

In the distance, I heard the howling.

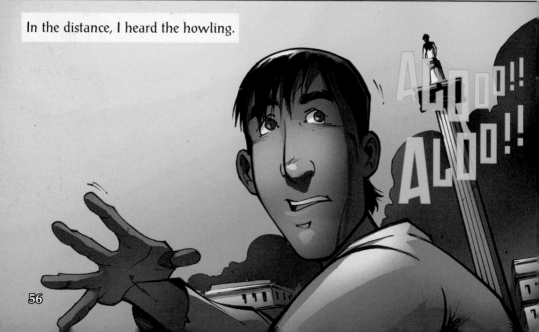

The howling got stronger. It sounded like someone pleading and sobbing.

I entered Regent's Park and over the trees saw the terrible creature.

As I approached, the howling stopped.

Without thinking, I ran towards the monster.

Suddenly, the machine began to fall.

ALOOOOO!!

I soon left London and set out for my little house in Woking.

It's still here! The Martians haven't destroyed it!

I stumbled into the hall, foolishly hoping that my wife had returned.

Upstairs, I found the article I'd been working on when the Martians came – but nothing else.

No one's here.

I never should have left her.

The war had ended. Not by the power of humans, but by one of the smallest creatures on Earth.

From the moment the invaders had arrived, our microscopic allies were already overthrowing them.

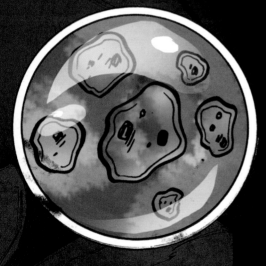

As disease killed millions of people throughout the ages, these same bacteria had killed every one of the invading Martians.

Our invisible companions had saved our lives and brought an end to this War of the Worlds.

About the Author

Herbert George Wells was born on 21 September, 1866, in Bromley, Kent. At age 7, he suffered a broken leg. While resting his injury, Wells started reading books. As he grew older, he continued to enjoy reading and school. At 14, young Wells quit school to help his struggling family. Fortunately, he received a scholarship in 1883 and began studying science at a school in London. Soon after, Wells started writing. Some of his works, like *The War of the Worlds*, combine his love for storytelling and science.

About the Retelling Authors

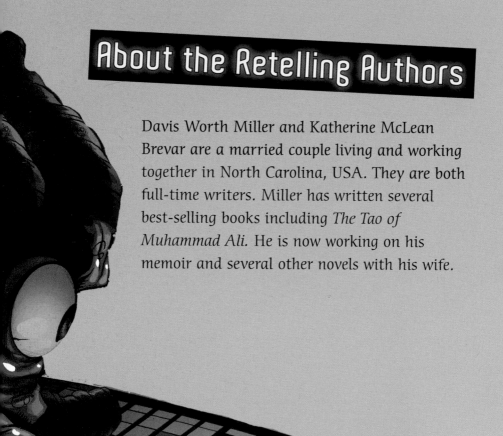

Davis Worth Miller and Katherine McLean Brevar are a married couple living and working together in North Carolina, USA. They are both full-time writers. Miller has written several best-selling books including *The Tao of Muhammad Ali*. He is now working on his memoir and several other novels with his wife.

Glossary

abandoned (ah-BAN-duhnd) - empty, or no longer in use

allies (AL-eyes) - people or things that give support and help to another

bacteria (bak-TIHR-ee-ah) - microscopic living things that sometimes cause disease

crater (KRAY-tur) - a large hole in the ground often caused by an explosion

curate (KYOOR-ayt) - a person in charge of a church

cylinder (SIL-uhn-dur) - a shape with flat, circular ends and sides shaped like the outside of a tube

gravity (GRAV-ih-tee) - the force that pulls things down towards Earth and keeps them from floating into space

Martians (MAR-shuhns) - fictional alien creatures from the planet Mars

meteorite (MEE-tee-ur-rite) - the part of a meteor or space rock that falls to Earth before it has burned up

microscopic (mye-kroh-SKOP-ik) - too small to be seen without a microscope

tentacle (TEN-tuh-kuhl) - one of the long, flexible limbs of some animals, such as an octopus

An Invasion from Mars!

On 30 October, 1938, an announcer for an American radio station started his broadcast with a warning. He told his listeners that for the next 60 minutes they'd be hearing a play based on the H. G. Wells novel, *The War of the Worlds*. Unfortunately, many people tuned in late and never heard the introduction.

As the show started, the radio's music was quickly interrupted by a breaking news bulletin. It said a "huge flaming object" had struck a farm near Grover's Mill, New Jersey, USA. A reporter on the scene described seeing an alien crawl out of a spacecraft. "Good heavens, something's wriggling out of the shadow," he said. "I can see the thing's body now. It's large - large as a bear. It glistens like wet leather."

Later reports detailed that Newark, New Jersey, had been destroyed by Martian invaders. The reports stated that the aliens were on their way to New York City, which was being evacuated. Other flaming objects and invaders had been spotted near Washington, Buffalo, Chicago, and other cities around the United States.

Of course, all of these "reports" of aliens were just part of the radio show. Still, thousands of people believed the attacks were real. They called newspapers, radio stations, and police headquarters, asking how to protect themselves from the aliens.

Hundreds of people needed medical treatment for shock. Terrified listeners hid in their cellars and loaded their rifles. In the area around New York City, highways became jammed with cars. Train and bus stations were choked with terrified people trying to leave the city.

In all, about one million people believed that they were listening to a real alien invasion. As the show ended, those people soon realized that they had been tricked. The entire show was simply a Halloween gag performed by 23-year-old Orson Welles and a group of actors. Welles would later become one of the most famous movie directors in Hollywood.

Discussion Questions

1. On page 21, George leaves his wife to go and hunt for the Martians. Do you think this was a good decision? Or, do you think he should have stayed with her? Explain your answer.

2. At the end of the story, the Martians that came to Earth are defeated. Do you think more of them will come? Why or why not?

3. This story is fiction, but do you think aliens really exist? Do you think they will ever come to Earth? Will they be good or evil? Explain your answers.

Writing Prompts

1. An alien spacecraft has just landed in your town! Would you be friendly to the aliens or try to make them go away? Write a story about what you would do.

2. Describe what you think an alien creature would look like. When you're finished writing out the description, give it to a friend. Have him or her draw a picture of the creature based on your description. Did the alien turn out like you had imagined?

3. The aliens in this book came from Mars. Describe what you think the cities on their planet look like. Where do the aliens live? Where do they eat? Do the alien kids go to school?

The Hound of the Baskervilles

Late one night, Sir Charles Baskerville is attacked outside his castle in Dartmoor, Devon. Could it be the Hound of the Baskervilles, a legendary creature that haunts the nearby moor? Sherlock Holmes, the world's greatest detective, is on the case.

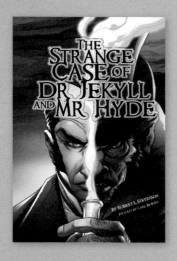

The Strange Case of Dr Jekyll and Mr Hyde

Scientist Dr Henry Jekyll believes every human has two minds: one good and one evil. He develops a potion to separate them from each other. Soon, his evil mind takes over, and Dr Jekyll becomes a hideous fiend known as Mr Hyde.

20,000 Leagues Under the Sea

Scientist Pierre Aronnax and his trusty servant set sail to hunt a sea monster. With help from Ned Land, the world's greatest harpooner, the men soon discover that the creature is really a high-tech submarine. To keep this secret from being revealed, the sub's leader, Captain Nemo, takes the men hostage. Now, each man must decide whether to trust Nemo or try to escape this underwater world.

Dracula

On a business trip to Transylvania, Jonathan Harker stays at an eerie castle owned by a man named Count Dracula. When strange things start to happen, Harker investigates and finds the count sleeping in a coffin! Harker isn't safe, and when the count escapes to London, neither are his friends.

Graphic Revolve

If you have enjoyed this story, there are many more exciting tales for you to discover in the Graphic Revolve collection...

20,000 Leagues Under the Sea

Black Beauty

Dracula

Frankenstein

Gulliver's Travels

The Hound of the Baskervilles

The Hunchback of Notre Dame

King Arthur and the Knights of the Round Table

Robin Hood

The Strange Case of Dr Jekyll and Mr Hyde

Treasure Island

The War of the Worlds